Adding and Subtracting

How to use this book with your child:

It is recommended that an adult spends time with a child while doing any kind of school practice, to offer encouragement and guidance. Find a quiet place to work, preferably at a table, and encourage your child to hold his or her pen or pencil correctly.

Try to work at your child's pace and avoid spending too long on any one page or activity. Most of all, emphasise the fun element of what you are doing and enjoy this special and exciting time!

Don't forget to add your reward sticker to each page you complete!

Reward
sticker!

Designed by Plum5
Illustrations by Sue King, Sharon Smart and Andy Geeson
Educational consultant Josh Levenson and Nina Filipek

www.autumnchildrensbooks.co.uk

Number bonds to 10

Do you know your numbers bonds to 10?
Write the missing numbers in the boxes.

$7 + \boxed{3} = 10$

$8 + \boxed{2} = 10$

$9 + \boxed{4} = 10$

$4 + \boxed{} = 10$

$5 + \boxed{} = 10$

Reward sticker!

☐ + 3 = 10

☐ + 6 = 10

☐ + 1 = 10

☐ + 5 = 10

2 + ☐ = 10

Addition on the farm

Complete these farmyard sums by writing the missing numbers in the boxes.

$\boxed{}$ + 7 = 12

$\boxed{}$ + 4 = 8

7 + $\boxed{}$ = 14

4 + 3 = $\boxed{}$

$\boxed{}$ + 10 = 20

$\boxed{}$ + 9 = 10

Reward sticker!

$2 + \boxed{} = 4$ $\qquad$ $7 + 9 = \boxed{}$

$\boxed{} + 7 = 19$ $\qquad$ $\boxed{} + 11 = 11$

$8 + \boxed{} = 21$ $\qquad$ $18 + 12 = \boxed{}$

$\boxed{} + 7 = 15$ $\qquad$ $\boxed{} + 8 = 17$

Reward sticker!

5

Alien addition

Solve these space sums. Write the answers in the boxes.

15 + 3 = ☐

16 + 2 = ☐

11 + 3 = ☐

18 + 7 = ☐

15 + 9 = ☐

13 + 4 = ☐

Reward sticker!

26 + 7 = ☐

23 + 9 = ☐

18 + 5 = ☐

91 + 8 = ☐

48 + 3 = ☐

35 + 6 = ☐

67 + 7 = ☐

55 + 6 = ☐

Reward sticker!

Missing numbers

The answers to these sums are missing. Write in the answers to complete the sums using the numbers in the balloons.

34 + 6 =

83 + 7 =

77 + 3 =

78 + 4 =

53 + 9 =

23 + 6 =

45 + 7 =

88 + 5 =

13 + 9 =

22

82

90

29

62

52

93

40

80

Reward sticker!

Adding 10s

Work out these sums (they will help you in the next task!).

5 + 8 = ☐   6 + 3 = ☐

2 + 6 = ☐   5 + 1 = ☐

7 + 5 = ☐   8 + 3 = ☐

Now use the sums above to help you answer the questions below.
Hint: 4 + 3 = 7 so 40 + 30 = 70.
What do you notice about the answers?

50 + 80 = ☐   60 + 30 = ☐

20 + 60 = ☐   50 + 10 = ☐

70 + 50 = ☐   80 + 30 = ☐

Reward sticker!

Adding 100s

Work out these sums using what you learnt on the previous page.
Hint: **5 + 4 = 9** so **50 + 40 = 90** that means **500 + 400 = 900**!

300 + 200 = ☐   Hint: **3 + 2 = 5**

400 + 300 = ☐

200 + 700 = ☐

100 + 700 = ☐

200 + 500 = ☐

400 + 500 = ☐

Reward
sticker!

Match the answers

Draw lines to join the sums on the boats to the answers on the anchors.

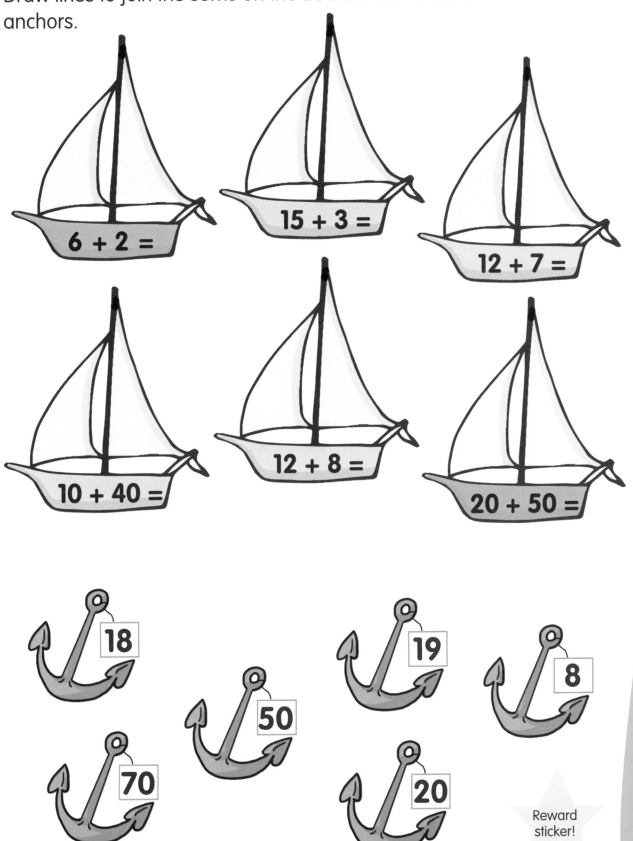

6 + 2 =

15 + 3 =

12 + 7 =

10 + 40 =

12 + 8 =

20 + 50 =

18

19

8

50

70

20

Reward sticker!

Double digits

Add the two digit numbers together and write your answers in the boxes. If you need to, use a spare piece of paper to work them out.

35 + 22 = ☐

43 + 36 = ☐

25 + 42 = ☐

65 + 24 = ☐

52 + 34 = ☐

76 + 22 = ☐

23 + 51 = ☐

43 + 17 = ☐

67 + 28 = ☐

37 + 51 = ☐

Reward sticker!

It all adds up

Add the three digit numbers to the two digit numbers and write your answers in the boxes.

178 + 45 = ☐

259 + 52 = ☐

444 + 63 = ☐

153 + 70 = ☐

456 + 16 = ☐

322 + 26 = ☐

244 + 55 = ☐

101 + 23 = ☐

Reward sticker!

Addition test

Now take the addition test. Do the sums and write the answers in the boxes.

11 + 2 = ☐   6 + 7 = ☐

10 + 5 = ☐   3 + 12 = ☐

A boy has **5** sweets and a girl has **7** sweets. How many sweets do they have altogether?  ☐

21 + 6 = ☐   20 + 8 = ☐

17 + 7 = ☐   12 + 6 = ☐

One alien has **8** eyes and another alien has **9** eyes. How many eyes do they have altogether? ☐

Reward sticker!

13 + 12 = ☐   20 + 16 = ☐

34 + 23 = ☐   42 + 16 = ☐

48 + 31 = ☐   57 + 22 = ☐

68 + 26 = ☐   45 + 37 = ☐

465 + 4 = ☐

353 + 6 = ☐

272 + 7 = ☐

756 + 7 = ☐

Reward sticker!

Fact families

Here is a fact family for 8 + 6 = 14.

- 8 + 6 = 14
- 6 + 8 = 14
- 14 − 6 = 8
- 14 − 8 = 6

Complete the following fact families:

- 8 + 9 = 17
- ___ + ___ = ___

- ___ − ___ = ___
- ___ − ___ = ___

- 9 + 5 = 14
- ___ + ___ = ___

- ___ − ___ = ___
- ___ − ___ = ___

- 5 + 7 = 12
- ___ + ___ = ___

- ___ − ___ = ___
- ___ − ___ = ___

Reward sticker!

Here is a fact family for 13 + 7 = 20.

- $13 + 7 = 20$
- $7 + 13 = 20$
- $20 - 7 = 13$
- $20 - 13 = 7$

Complete the following fact families:

- $8 + 5 = 13$
- $\_\_ + \_\_ = \_\_$

- $\_\_ - \_\_ = \_\_$
- $\_\_ - \_\_ = \_\_$

- $13 + 3 = 16$
- $\_\_ + \_\_ = \_\_$

- $\_\_ - \_\_ = \_\_$
- $\_\_ - \_\_ = \_\_$

- $11 + 4 = 15$
- $\_\_ + \_\_ = \_\_$

- $\_\_ - \_\_ = \_\_$
- $\_\_ - \_\_ = \_\_$

Reward sticker!

Penguin subtraction

Work out the subtractions and write the answers on the penguins.

6 – 3 =

8 – 7 =

11 – 2 =

13 – 7 =

15 – 9 =

16 – 8 =

9 – 4 =

10 – 6 =

Reward
sticker!

Missing numbers

Complete the subtractions by filling in the missing numbers.

3 − ☐ = 0   21 − ☐ = 14

☐ − 4 = 8   15 − 5 = ☐

17 − ☐ = 9   12 − ☐ = 9

☐ − 9 = 0   18 − 10 = ☐

5 − ☐ = 4   20 − ☐ = 10

Bubble subtractions

Complete the subtractions by filling in the missing numbers.

$11 - \boxed{} = 5$

$\boxed{} - 5 = 7$

$\boxed{} - 7 = 6$

$\boxed{} - 4 = 8$

$14 - \boxed{} = 9$

$\boxed{} - 5 = 17$

$\boxed{} - 7 = 16$

Reward
sticker!

Subtraction in space

Work out the subtractions and write the answers in the boxes.

79 – 6 =

88 – 5 =

99 – 8 =

56 – 4 =

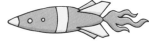

49 – 3 =

37 – 5 =

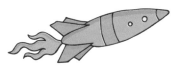

78 – 4 =

29 – 8 =

Reward
sticker!

Subtraction is magic!

Complete the subtractions by taking a one digit number away from a two digit number. Write your answers in the boxes.

49 − 5 =

37 − 6 =

55 − 3 =

28 − 6 =

67 − 4 =

23 − 9 =

76 − 8 =

54 − 5 =

Reward sticker!

Double digits

Complete the subtractions by taking a two digit number away from another two digit number. Write your answers in the boxes.

79 – 16 = ☐   83 – 19 = ☐

27 – 11 = ☐   56 – 12 = ☐

49 – 13 = ☐   57 – 17 = ☐

23 – 13 = ☐   40 – 28 = ☐

Reward sticker!

Fun with subtractions

Solve these problems and write the answers in the boxes.

Take **4** bananas away from these monkeys. How many bananas are left?

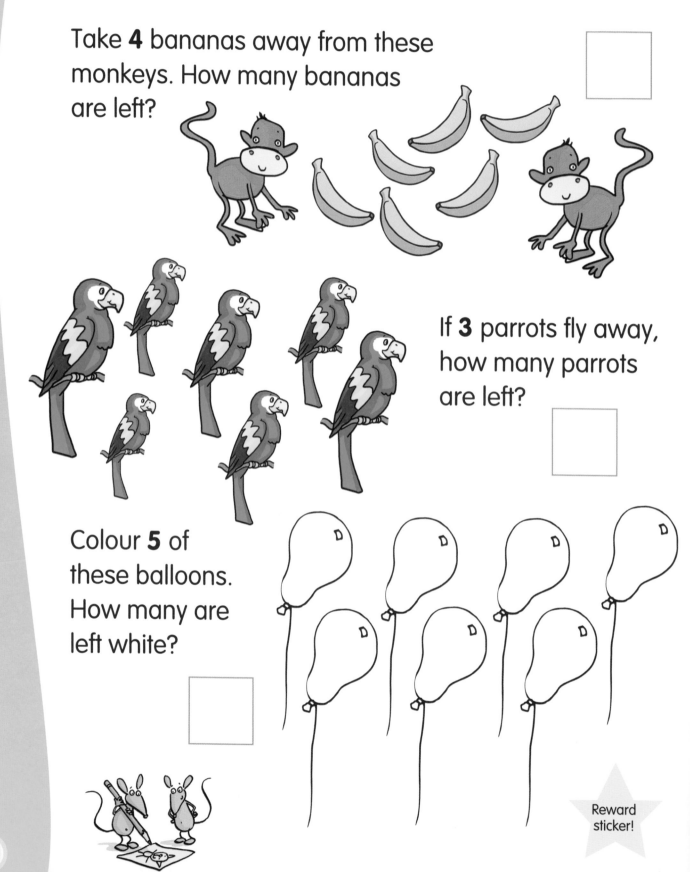

If **3** parrots fly away, how many parrots are left?

Colour **5** of these balloons. How many are left white?

Reward sticker!

A rabbit eats **4** carrots.
How many carrots are left?

Draw **8** lit candles on this cake.

If Molly blows out **3** candles, how many lit candles are left?

Reward sticker!

Butterfly subtractions

Do the subtractions and write the answers in the boxes.

90 – 6 = ⬜ 60 – 3 = ⬜

40 – 4 = ⬜ 30 – 8 = ⬜

50 – 5 = ⬜ 44 – 7 = ⬜

33 – 5 = ⬜ 52 – 7 = ⬜

Reward sticker!

78 – 9 = [ ]   63 – 6 = [ ]

83 – 9 = [ ]   14 – 12 = [ ]

55 – 16 = [ ]   77 – 17 = [ ]

28 – 13 = [ ]   84 – 18 = [ ]

Reward
sticker!

Super subtractions

Try taking a one digit number away from a three digit number.
Write your answers in the boxes.

537 – 5 = ☐   648 – 6 = ☐

354 – 3 = ☐   192 – 6 = ☐

746 – 8 = ☐   371 – 5 = ☐

823 – 8 = ☐   342 – 7 = ☐

185 – 9 = ☐   203 – 8 = ☐

Reward
sticker!

Subtraction test

Now take the subtraction test. Do the subtractions and write the answers in the boxes.

13 – 8 = ☐   11 – 1 = ☐

15 – 9 = ☐   18 – 6 = ☐

A boy has **8** sweets and he eats **5**. How many sweets does he have left? ☐

14 – 12 = ☐   17 – 8 = ☐

22 – 10 = ☐   24 – 5 = ☐

25 rabbits are sitting in a field and **9** run away. How many rabbits are left? ☐

Subtraction test 2

29 − 7 = ☐   37 − 6 = ☐

58 − 3 = ☐   98 − 8 = ☐

48 − 12 = ☐   27 − 15 = ☐

65 − 16 = ☐   39 − 19 = ☐

423 − 4 = ☐

275 − 3 = ☐

739 − 8 = ☐

456 − 9 = ☐

Reward
sticker!

Answers

Number bonds to 10
7 + **3** = 10
8 + **2** = 10
9 + **1** = 10
4 + **6** = 10
5 + **5** = 10

7 + 3 = 10
4 + 6 = 10
9 + 1 = 10
5 + 5 = 10
2 + **8** = 10

Addition on the farm
5 + 7 = 12
4 + 4 = 8
7 + **7** = 14
4 + 3 = **7**
10 + 10 = 20
1 + 9 = 10

2 + **2** = 4
7 + 9 = **16**
12 + 7 = 19
0 + 11 = 11
8 + **13** = 21
18 + 12 = **30**
8 + 7 = 15
9 + 8 = 17

Alien addition
15 + 3 = **18**
16 + 2 = **18**
11 + 3 = **14**
18 + 7 = **25**
15 + 9 = **24**
13 + 4 = **17**

26 + 7 = **33**
23 + 9 = **32**
18 + 5 = **23**
91 + 8 = **99**
48 + 3 = **51**
35 + 6 = **41**
67 + 7 = **74**
55 + 6 = **61**

Missing numbers
34 + 6 = **40**
83 + 7 = **90**
77 + 3 = **80**
78 + 4 = **82**
53 + 9 = **62**
23 + 6 = **29**
45 + 7 = **52**
88 + 5 = **93**
13 + 9 = **22**

Adding 10s
5 + 8 = **13**
6 + 3 = **9**
2 + 6 = **8**
5 + 1 = **6**
7 + 5 = **12**
8 + 3 = **11**

50 + 80 = **130**
60 + 30 = **90**
20 + 60 = **80**
50 + 10 = **60**
70 + 50 = **120**
80 + 30 = **110**

Adding 100s
300 + 200 = **500**
400 + 300 = **700**
200 + 700 = **900**
100 + 700 = **800**
200 + 500 = **700**
400 + 500 = **900**

Match the answers
6 + 2 = **8**
15 + 3 = **18**
12 + 7 = **19**
10 + 40 = **50**
12 + 8 = **20**
20 + 50 = **70**

Double digits
35 + 22 = **57**
43 + 36 = **79**
25 + 42 = **67**
65 + 24 = **89**
52 + 34 = **86**
76 + 22 = **98**
23 + 51 = **74**
43 + 17 = **60**
67 + 28 = **95**
37 + 51 = **88**

It all adds up
178 + 45 = **223**
259 + 52 = **311**
444 + 63 = **507**
153 + 70 = **223**
456 + 16 = **472**
322 + 26 = **348**
244 + 55 = **299**
101 + 23 = **124**

Addition test
11 + 2 = **13**
6 + 7 = **13**
10 + 5 = **15**
3 + 12 = **15**
12 sweets
21 + 6 = **27**
20 + 8 = **28**
17 + 7 = **24**
12 + 6 = **18**
17 eyes

13 + 12 = **25**
20 + 16 = **36**
34 + 23 = **57**
42 + 16 = **58**
48 + 31 = **79**
57 + 22 = **79**
68 + 26 = **94**
45 + 37 = **82**
465 + 4 = **469**
353 + 6 = **359**
272 + 7 = **279**
756 + 7 = **763**

Answers

Fact families

8 + 9 = 17   **9** + **8** = 17
17 − **9** = **8**   **17** − **8** = **9**

9 + 5 = 14   **5** + **9** = 14
14 − **5** = **9**   **14** − **9** = **5**

5 + 7 = 12   **7** + **5** = 12
12 − **7** = **5**   **12** − **5** = **7**

8 + 5 = 13   **5** + **8** = 13
13 − **5** = **8**   **13** − **8** = **5**

13 + 3 = 16   **3** + **13** = 16
16 − **3** = **13**   **16** − **13** = **3**

11 + 4 = 15   **4** + **11** = 15
15 − **4** = **11**   **15** − **11** = **4**

Penguin subtraction

6 − 3 = **3**
8 − 7 = **1**
11 − 2 = **9**
13 − 7 = **6**
15 − 9 = **6**
16 − 8 = **8**
9 − 4 = **5**
10 − 6 = **4**

Missing numbers

3 − **3** = 0
21 − **7** = 14
12 − 4 = 8
15 − 5 = **10**
17 − **8** = 9
12 − **3** = 9
9 − 9 = 0
18 − 10 = **8**
5 − **1** = 4
20 − **10** = 10

Bubble subtractions

11 − **6** = 5
12 − 5 = 7
13 − 7 = 6
12 − 4 = 8
14 − **5** = 9
22 − 5 = 17
23 − 7 = 16

Subtraction in space

79 − 6 = **73**
88 − 5 = **83**
99 − 8 = **91**
56 − 4 = **52**
49 − 3 = **46**
37 − 5 = **32**
78 − 4 = **74**
29 − 8 = **21**

Subtraction is magic!

49 − 5 = **44**
37 − 6 = **31**
55 − 3 = **52**
28 − 6 = **22**
67 − 4 = **63**
23 − 9 = **14**
76 − 8 = **68**
54 − 5 = **49**

Double digits

79 − 16 = **63**
83 − 19 = **64**
27 − 11 = **16**
56 − 12 = **44**
49 − 13 = **36**
57 − 17 = **40**
23 − 13 = **10**
40 − 28 = **12**

Fun with subtractions

2 bananas
4 parrots
2 balloons
4 carrots
5 candles

Butterfly subtractions

90 − 6 = **84**
60 − 3 = **57**
40 − 4 = **36**
30 − 8 = **22**
50 − 5 = **45**
44 − 7 = **37**
33 − 5 = **28**
52 − 7 = **45**
78 − 9 = **69**
63 − 6 = **57**
83 − 9 = **74**

14 − 12 = **2**
55 − 16 = **39**
77 − 17 = **60**
28 − 13 = **15**
84 − 18 = **66**

Super subtractions

537 − 5 = **532**
648 − 6 = **642**
354 − 3 = **351**
192 − 6 = **186**
746 − 8 = **738**
371 − 5 = **366**
823 − 8 = **815**
342 − 7 = **335**
185 − 9 = **176**
203 − 8 = **195**

Subtraction test

13 − 8 = **5**
11 − 1 = **10**
15 − 9 = **6**
18 − 6 = **12**
3 sweets
14 − 12 = **2**
17 − 8 = **9**
22 − 10 = **12**
24 − 5 = **19**
16 rabbits

Subtraction test 2

29 − 7 = **22**
37 − 6 = **31**
58 − 3 = **55**
98 − 8 = **90**
48 − 12 = **36**
27 − 15 = **12**
65 − 16 = **49**
39 − 19 = **20**
423 − 4 = **419**
275 − 3 = **272**
739 − 8 = **731**
456 − 9 = **447**